Buster Books

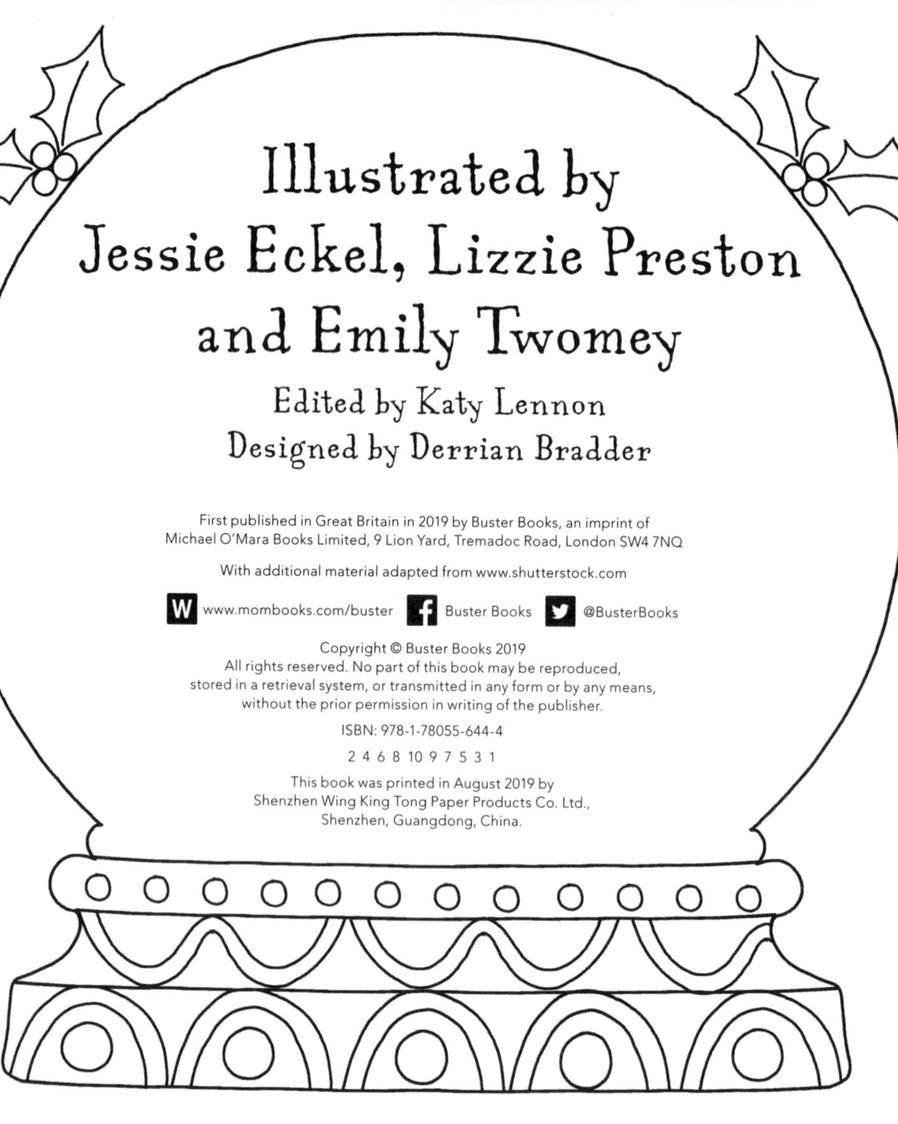

Illustrated by
Jessie Eckel, Lizzie Preston
and Emily Twomey

Edited by Katy Lennon
Designed by Derrian Bradder

First published in Great Britain in 2019 by Buster Books, an imprint of
Michael O'Mara Books Limited, 9 Lion Yard, Tremadoc Road, London SW4 7NQ

With additional material adapted from www.shutterstock.com

W www.mombooks.com/buster  Buster Books  @BusterBooks



ISBN: 978-1-78055-644-4

2 4 6 8 10 9 7 5 3 1

This book was printed in August 2019 by
Shenzhen Wing King Tong Paper Products Co. Ltd.,
Shenzhen, Guangdong, China.